# Sweden
# Coloring Book

by Kirsten Sevig

*A big TACK SÅ MYCKET to Lisa HAMNES & ELSE Sevig!*

Published by
Skandisk, Inc.
Bloomington, Minnesota

D1710936

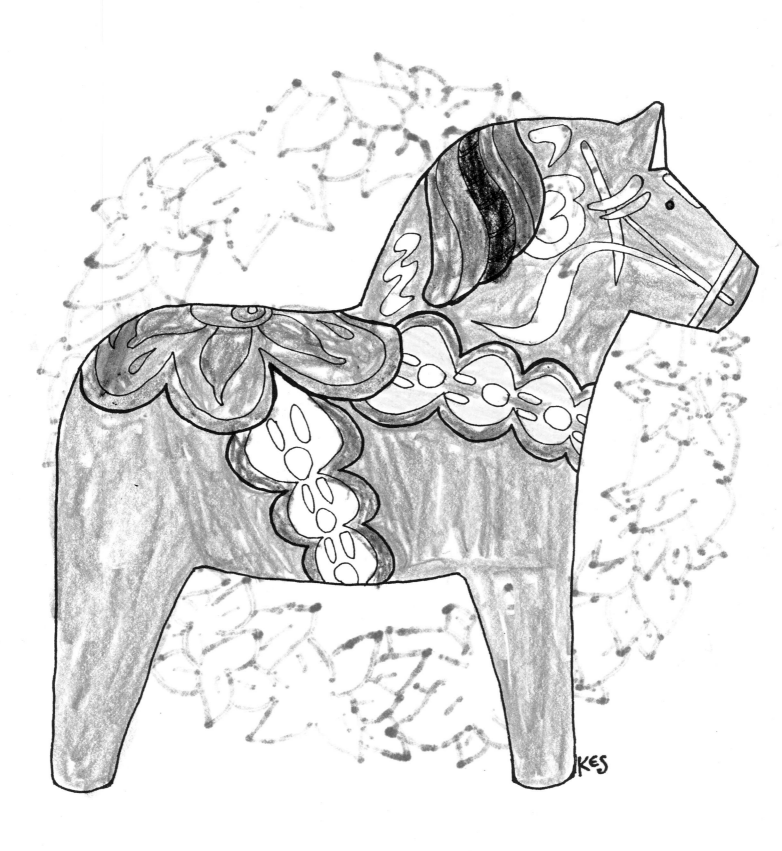

The ***Dalahäst* (Dala horse)** is the most recognized symbol of
Sweden.  These colorful painted wooden horses are named after
the Swedish province where they originated—Dalarna.

Like the Dala horse, the **Dalatupp (Dala rooster)** is also
carved out of wood and painted in bright colors.  It is believed
that a Dala rooster in the kitchen will bring good luck to the cook.

**Läckö Castle** on Lake Vänern is one of many castles in Sweden. It was built in the 17th century and is a major tourist attraction.

Stockholm's ***Gamla Stan* (Old Town)** has narrow cobblestone streets and hidden courtyards where you can find a wide variety of shops and restaurants.

This is Tor and his son, Per.  Viking boys used play weapons to prepare for battle.  Vikings were merchants, farmers, explorers, and warriors.

Helga the Viking runs the farm and the house.  As she spins wool
into yarn, she teaches her daughter, Signe, to embroider.

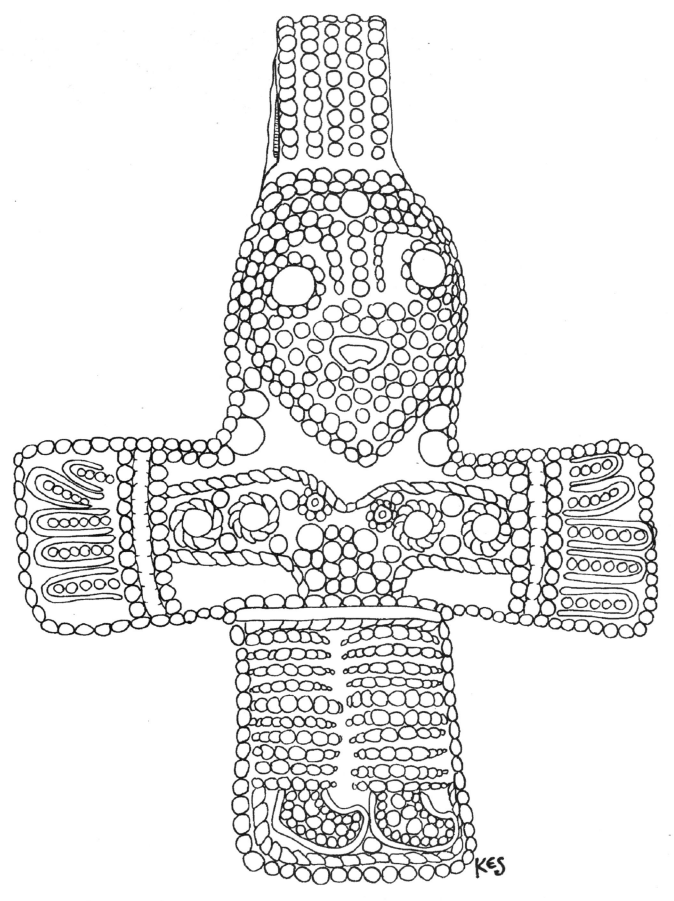

This crucifix was made out of silver in about 900. It was found
in a Viking woman's grave in **Birka**, Sweden's first Viking town.

Erik is sailing his Viking ship.

This motif is from the oldest tapestry in Sweden. It was woven in
the 12th-century, and once hung in Skog Church in Hälsingland.

Chip carving is a popular form of woodcarving in Sweden.
A geometrical pattern is made by carving away small chips of
wood.  This trivet was chip-carved from a piece of ash.

On Maundy Thursday or Easter Eve, Karin and Greta dress like *Påskkäringar* (Easter Witches) with soot on their faces. They go door-to-door shouting *Glad påsk* (Happy Easter), and often receive treats. This is a reminder of a Swedish legend that witches are stirring at Eastertime.

# Påskris or Fastlagsris
## Easter (or Lent) Branches

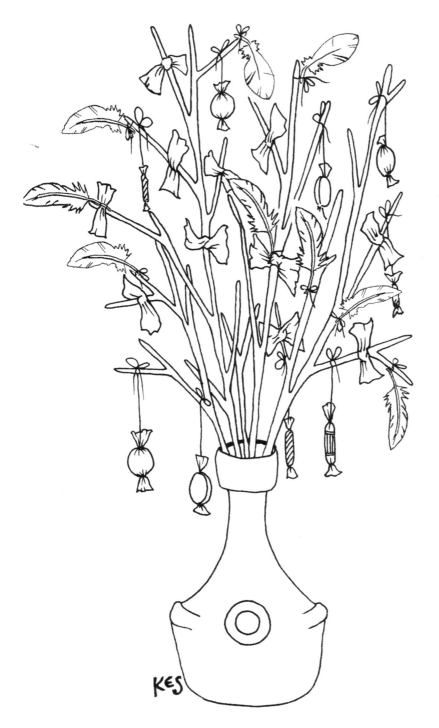

During Lent in Sweden birch branches are decorated with brightly colored feathers. They are called **Påskris** *or Easter Branches*. Sometimes they are called *Fastlagsris* or *Lent Branches*. Traditionally these branches were used to wake people up on **Fettisdagen (Fat Tuesday)**, the Tuesday before Lent. According to ancient beliefs, the birch branches were thought to hasten the arrival of spring. Today they are used simply as a festive decoration.

Children especially enjoy helping to decorate the branches for this colorful display.

To make your own *Påskris*, you will need to cut branches from trees or bushes—lilacs or birch branches work well. Use natural branches or spray them with gold spray paint. Do this outside with the help of an adult. When the branches are dry, place them in a vase with water.

Decorate each branch with five or six brightly-colored feathers (available in craft stores). Colorful curling ribbon and tissue paper bows can also be added. To make tissue paper bows, cut up tissue paper in a variety of colors making rectangles about 3 by 6 inches. Twist the tissue paper around the branches so it will stay—wrap around once, then give two twists. Some families like to add candy hung with ribbon to the branches as a special treat for the children.

Lisa and Olle and their neighbors join in a ***Midsommar* (Midsummer)** parade to the maypole for dancing & singing on the longest day of the year (around June 21st).

Folkdancing is popular in Sweden. Viktoria and Ulrik are dressed in costumes from **Skåne** in southern Sweden. Viktoria has a dark blue bodice and a red skirt. Ulrik is wearing a red vest. His knickers are yellow, and his socks are blue.

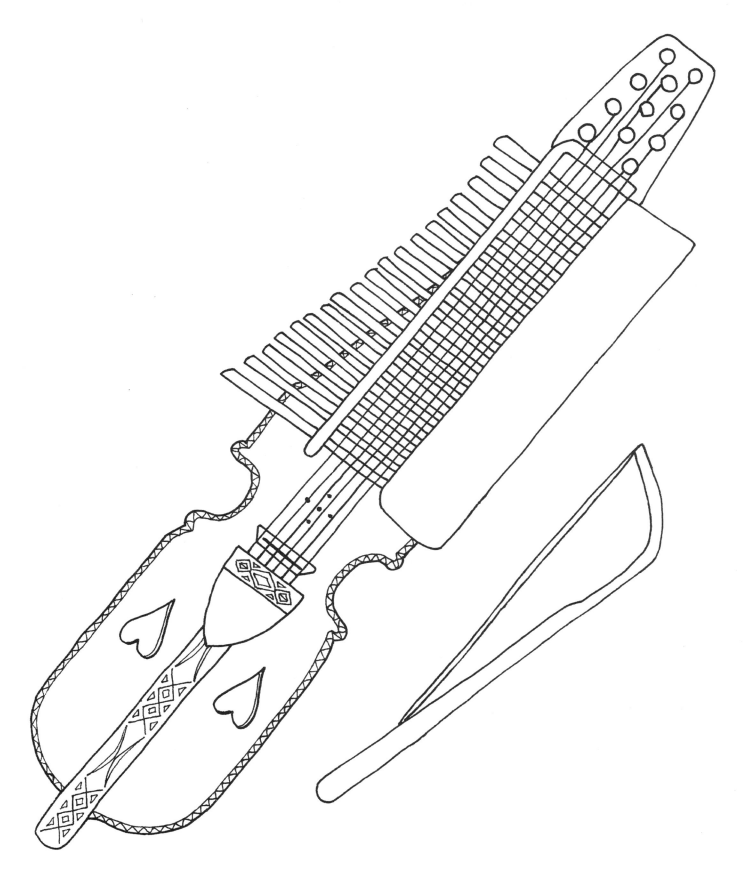

The ***Nyckelharpa* (Swedish keyed fiddle)** is a traditional Swedish instrument that dates back to the 12th century. It is a stringed instrument but it also has wooden keys that press down on the strings. The keys are pressed with the left hand while the right hand wields a short bow. *Nyckel* is Swedish for "key."

Trolls are a popular subject of Swedish folklore. These two
frightening trolls have curly hair and many warts.

Elle-Kari wishes her father good luck before the reindeer events
begin at the traditional **Sami** fair in **Jokkmokk**, Lappland.
Today the Sami live in Finland, Norway, Russia, and Sweden.
They have their own national anthem and national flag.

This decorated purse is part of a Swedish
folk costume from Älvedalen, Dalarna.

***Träskor* (clogs)** from Sweden are popular all over the world.  They are made of leather with a wooden sole.  This pair is decorated with *dalmålning*.

***Dalmålning* (dala painting)** originated in the province of Dalarna in the 1700s.
Snarf Anders Andersson painted this horseback rider in 1820.

Floral arrangements are another popular form of **dalmålning (dala painting)**, a type of Swedish folk painting.

***The Wonderful Adventures of Nils***, written by Selma Lagerlöf
(1858-1940) in 1907, is one of Sweden's best-loved children's books.
Here you see Nils on his goose flying over Sweden.  Selma Lagerlöf was
the first woman to receive the Nobel Prize in Literature.

***Pippi Långstrump* (Pippi Longstocking)** was created by Swedish author Astrid Lindgren (1907-2002) in 1945. The stories about Pippi are as popular today as they were when they were written. Pippi, a nine-year-old girl, is the strongest little girl in the world. She lives with her horse and her monkey in her own house in Sweden.

The **Vasa** warship was built in the 1620s and was decorated with gold leaf and 700 sculptures and carvings. The ship sank in Stockholm Harbor on her maiden voyage in 1628. It has been salvaged and restored and now has its own museum in Stockholm.

This ***Väderkvarn* (windmill)** is one of many found on the island of Öland, in the Baltic Sea off the east coast of Sweden.

**Carl Larsson** (1853-1919) was a famous Swedish artist. The title of this painting is *Lars-Erik Lamm*. It was painted in 1917.

**Carl Larsson** and his wife Karin, who was also an artist, lived in a farmhouse in Dalarna with their eight children. This girl in a Dala costume was painted in 1912.

ABBA®

Still popular today, the Swedish pop-rock group **ABBA** was formed in 1973. Their name came from the initials of the four singers: **A**gnetha Fältskog, **B**enny Andersson, **B**jörn Ulvaeus, and **A**nni-Frid Lyngstad. Their many hits included *Dancing Queen, Fernando, Super-Trouper* and *Take a Chance on Me*. The recent smash hit musical *Mama Mia* is based on ABBA's original songs.

**Bjørn Borg** is a world-champion tennis player from Sweden.
He led Sweden to its first Davis Cup win in 1975, and went on to
win six French Opens and five straight Wimbledons (1976-80).

Anna is wearing a white gown with a red sash and has a crown of candles on her head. She is dressed as *Sankta Lucia* **(Saint Lucia)**, the symbol of light and hope. On December 13th, **Lucia Day**, the oldest daughter in the family serves *Pepparkakor, Lussekatter* **(Lucia buns)**, and coffee while singing the song *Sankta Lucia*.

# Sankta Lucia  Saint Lucia

Text: Arvid Rosén
Melody: Neopolitan Folk Tune
Translation: Anne-Charlotte Harvey

1. Natten går tunga fjät
   runt gård och stuva.
   Kring jord, som sol'n förlät,
   skuggorna ruva.
   Då i vårt mörka hus
   stiger med tända ljus
   Sankta Lucia, Sankta Lucia.

2. Natten är stor och stum.
   Nu hör det svingar
   i alla tysta rum
   sus som av vingar.
   Se, på vår tröskel står
   vitklädd, med ljus i hår
   Sankta Lucia, Sankta Lucia.

3. "Mörkret skall flykta snart
   ur jordens dalar."
   Så hon ett underbart
   ord till oss talar.
   Dagen skall åter ny
   stiga ur rosig sky.
   Sankta Lucia, Sankta Lucia.

1. The night walks with heavy steps
   'round farm and cottage.
   Around the earth, forsaken by the sun,
   shadows are brooding.
   Then into our dark house
   steps with lighted candles
   Saint Lucia, Saint Lucia.

2. The night is vast and mute.
   Now hear reverberate
   in all silent rooms
   a rustle as of wings.
   See, on our threshold stands,
   dressed in white, lights in her hair,
   Saint Lucia, Saint Lucia.

3. "The darkness will soon leave
   the valleys of earth."
   Thus she a wonderful
   word to us speaks.
   The day shall again, reborn,
   rise from a rosy sky.
   Saint Lucia, Saint Lucia.

# *Pepparkakor* *(Ginger Cookies)*

The inviting scent of these cookies baking is part of the wonderful smell of a Swedish Christmas. Traditionally these cookies are rolled as thin as possible. However, if you wish to make *pepparkakor* to hang as decorations we suggest rolling the dough a bit thicker (approximately 3/16") so they don't break as easily. Use red silk ribbon to hang decorated cookies on the tree or in the windows.

| | |
|---|---|
| ½ | **cup molasses** |
| ½ | **cup brown sugar** |
| ½ | **cup (1 stick) butter** |
| 1 | **egg (well beaten)** |
| 2¼ | **cups flour** |
| ¼ | **tsp. salt** |
| ¼ | **tsp. baking soda** |
| ½ | **tsp. ginger** |
| ½ | **tsp. cinnamon** |

Preheat oven to 350°.
Heat molasses in saucepan until boiling.
Boil 1 minute. Add sugar and butter.
Stir until melted. Cool. When molasses mixture is cool, beat in egg.
Transfer this mixture to a large mixing bowl.

In a separate bowl mix together flour, salt, baking soda, and spices. Gradually add the dry ingredients to the molasses mixture, mixing thoroughly after each addition. Cover with saran wrap and chill dough in refrigerator for several hours or overnight.

Remove some of the chilled dough and place on a lightly floured surface. Roll to desired thickness. Cut with lightly floured cookie cutters into various shapes (pigs, horses, roosters, hearts, angels, and stars are common in Sweden). Use a straw to make a hole at the top for hanging before putting in the oven to bake. Place on ungreased cookie sheets (line cookie sheets with parchment if desired), and bake for 6 to 8 minutes. Watch closely.

Carefully remove cookies to cooling racks to cool. Cookies may be decorated with a powdered sugar frosting (or ready-made decorating icing) applied through a cake decorating tip. Store cookies in air-tight containers. This recipe also works well for making a gingerbread house.

Britta, Karl, and Katja are celebrating **Lucia Day** (December 13th) by having a Lucia procession. Britta is dressed as *Sankta Lucia* **(Saint Lucia)**, and is bringing *Lussekatter* **(Lucia Buns)** and coffee to her family, escorted by Karl who is dressed as a *Stjärngosse* **(Star Boy)** and is carrying a tall star to light the way.

***Brita with Candles and Apples*** was painted by Swedish
artist Carl Larsson in 1900. His daughter Brita was the model.

# *Julgranskorg*
## *(Woven Heart Baskets)*

These traditional heart-shaped baskets are "woven" out of paper. They are fun to make, and can be hung on the Christmas tree or in a window. Often they are filled with small wrapped candies when hung on the tree. Follow these steps to make your own simple heart basket, or go online to www.stavanger-web.com/jul/christma.htm for easy instructions on how to make a woven paper heart basket.

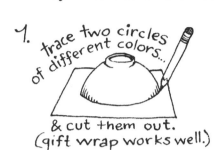   

1. trace two circles of different colors... & cut them out. (gift wrap works well.)

2. fold them in half.

3. glue them together & add a handle.

4. if you wish, you can add a sticker!

# *Svenska Plättar* *(Swedish Pancakes)*

There's nothing like pancakes to get you going on a cold winter morning. Swedish pancakes are typically very thin. They are served with jam and sometimes whipped cream!

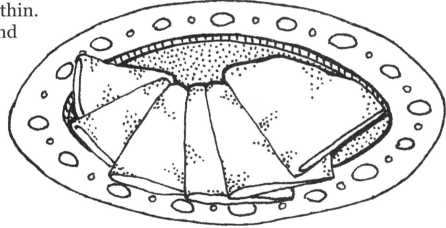

Ingredients:

**3   cups milk**
**½   tsp. salt**
**1   Tbsp. sugar**
**2   cups flour**
**2   eggs**

Beat together all ingredients with a whisk. Do not overbeat. If the batter is too thick, add a little milk; if too thin, add a little flour. Let sit 10 to 15 minutes before frying pancakes. Transfer cooked pancakes to a heated plate. To serve, spread with lingonberry preserves or strawberry jam, roll up and enjoy!                                    *Serves four.*

# Julgranskaramel
## (Christmas Tree Paper Candy)

Children in Sweden look forward to making these decorative tubes filled with holiday candy. They can be hung on the Christmas tree and opened on Christmas Eve!

## Supplies:

Card stock or other heavy paper (toilet-
   paper tubes may be used resulting in
   a somewhat larger version of the
   traditional *julgranskaramel*)
Tissue paper in assorted bright
   holiday colors
Individually-wrapped candies
Holiday stickers
Ribbon, tape, ruler, pencil, scissors

## Directions:

Cut the card stock into 4"x 4" squares. Roll each square into a cylinder about one inch in diameter and tape to hold (figure 1). Make as many cylinders as you wish and fill each with small wrapped candies. Cut tissue paper into approximately 5" x 15" pieces (adjust the size of the tissue paper to fit your cylinders). Lay two different colored sheets of tissue paper on top of each other.

Center a cylinder on the long side of the tissue paper (figure 2). Use a pencil to mark the edges of the cylinder, and draw a line on the tissue paper edge to edge at these marks. This will be your roll line. Fold the tissue paper along the roll line. Make accordion pleats on each end of the tissue paper up to each roll line (figure 3). Cut the pleated ends into a fringe about $1/4$" to $3/8$" thick (figure 4). Roll the cylinder inside the tissue paper and fasten with a holiday sticker (figure 5). Tie each end with ribbon and shake to fluff out the fringe. Tie a piece of yarn or ribbon to one or both ends for hanging (figure 6).

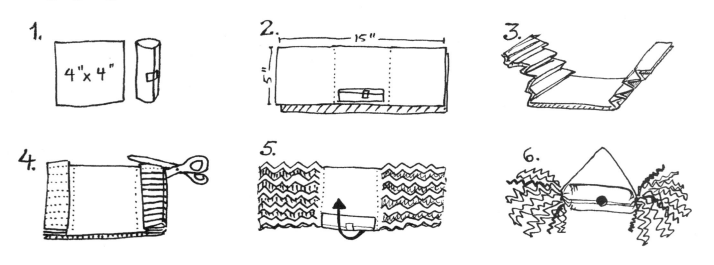

On Christmas Eve many Swedes set out a bowl of *julgröt* (**Christmas porridge**) for the *jultomten* (**Christmas elf**) to enjoy.

## *Julgröt* (Christmas Porridge)

This rice porridge is served at Christmas. Often an almond is hidden in the pudding. According to Swedish custom the person who finds the almond will marry within the next year. (If a child finds the almond it is said that their wish will come true.) When the porridge is served, each person makes up a rhyme as he or she takes a portion. This continues around the table until all the porridge is eaten.

- 1 **cup water**
- ¾ **cup medium grain rice**
- 1 **quart whole milk**
- ½ **tsp. salt**
- 1 **Tbsp. sugar**

Heat oven to 300° then turn it off!
Cook the rice in the water, allowing the rice to simmer under cover until the water has evaporated. Add milk and bring to a boil while stirring. Cover the pot and place it in the warm oven for about 1 1/2 hours.

Return the porridge to the stovetop and reheat while stirring. Add salt and sugar. Just before serving, stir in 1 whole blanched almond. Stir and serve with a spoon of heavy cream poured on top. Sprinkle with cinnamon and sugar.    *Serves four.*

# Karusellen The Carousel

Text & Melody: Traditional
Translation: Anne-Charlotte Harvey

1. Jungfru, jungfru, jungfru, jungfru skär,
   här är karusellen, som skall gå till kvällen.
   Tio för de stora och fem för de små.
   Skynda på, skynda på, nu skall karusellen gå!

REFRÄNG:
   :/: För ha ha ha, nu går det så bra
   för Andersson och Pettersson
   och Lundström å ja'! :/:

1. Maiden, maiden, maiden, maiden pure,
   here's the carousel which will go until evening.
   Ten for the big ones, and five for the small.
   Hurry up, hurry up, now the carousel is off!

CHORUS:
   :/: For he-he-he, it's fun as can be,
   for Andersson and Pettersson
   and Lundström and me! :/:

This song is used for dancing around the Christmas tree or the Maypole.

Children's books by **Elsa Beskow** (1874-1953), Sweden's beloved author and illustrator, have become classics. This is Kirsten Sevig's rendition of Elsa Beskow's illustration from her book ***Peter and Lotta's Christmas*** (1947). Here Peter and Lotta admire the Christmas tree while Aunt Brown and Aunt Green look on. Aunt Lavender plays the paino.
In Sweden the Christmas tree is often placed in the middle of the room so everyone can dance around it, singing songs like the one on the opposite page.

# Du gamla, du fria *Sweden's National Anthem*

Text: Richard Dybeck
Melody: Swedish Folk Tune
Singable Translation: Noel Wirén

1. Du gamla, du fria, du fjällhöga Nord,
   du tysta, du glädjerika, sköna!
   Jag hälsar dig, vänaste land uppå jord,
   din sol, din himmel, dina ängder gröna,
   din sol, din himmel, dina ängder gröna.

2. Du tronar på minnen från fornstora dar,
   då ärat ditt namn flög över jorden.
   Jag vet att du är och du blir vad du var.
   Ack, jag vill leva, jag vill dö i Norden!
   Ack, jag vill leva, jag vill dö i Norden!

1. Thou ancient, thou freeborn, thou mountainous North,
   In beauty and peace our hearts beguiling,
   I greet thee, thou loveliest land on the earth,
   Thy sun, thy skies, thy verdant meadows smiling,
   Thy sun, thy skies, thy verdant meadows smiling.

2. Thy throne rests on memories from great days of yore,
   When worldwide renown was valor's guerdon.
   I know to thy name thou art true as before.
   Oh, I would live and I would die in Sweden,
   Oh, I would live and die in Sweden.

**Sweden's National Coat of Arms** *(lilla riksvapnet)* dates back to 1336. It features three open gold crowns on a blue shield. The crown at the top is gold and the area behind it is red. Often the three crowns alone are used as a trademark for Sweden.

The Swedish flag has a yellow cross on a blue background.

# SWEDEN

Sweden is located in Scandinavia, a part of northern Europe. It is bordered on the east by Finland, and on the west by Norway. Sweden is a long narrow country (977 miles from north to south, and 350 miles wide at the widest point), with mountains in the north and lakes and forests throughout. Try to locate Sweden on a globe or in an atlas.

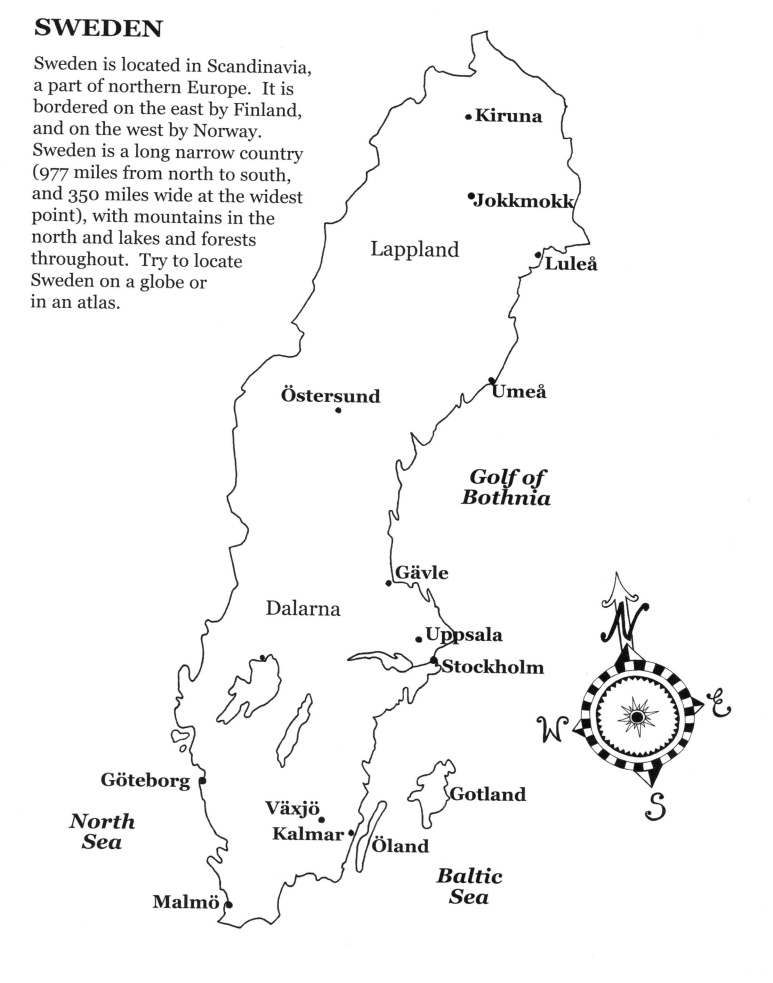

• Kiruna

• Jokkmokk

Lappland

• Luleå

Östersund •

Umeå •

**Golf of Bothnia**

• Gävle

Dalarna

• Uppsala

• Stockholm

Göteborg •

Gotland

**North Sea**

Växjö •
Kalmar •

Öland

**Baltic Sea**

Malmö •

# Favorite Resources to Learn More About Sweden:

## Sweden:

*Sweden in a Class of Its Own.* Egmont. (A photographic journey through Sweden, with information on her culture and traditions, history, people, and more.)

*Virtual Sweden Web Page.* www.Sweden.se (Sweden's official website for information about Sweden in English. Includes Swedish culture, history, travel, & many useful links.)

## Christmas in Sweden:

*Annika's Secret Wish.* Beverly Lewis. Illustrated by Pamela Querin. Bethany House Publishers. (A charming picture book set in turn-of-the-century Sweden, this story about finding the almond in the rice pudding captures the essence of a Swedish Christmas.)

*Christmas in Noisy Village.* Astrid Lindgren. Illustrated by Ilon Wikland. Penguin Books. (Share the joys of young children in Sweden as they prepare for Christmas. Ages 3-8.)

*How to Make a Swedish Christmas.* Helen Ingeborg. Pinstripe Press. (An excellent book that explains Swedish Christmas traditions, and includes craft patterns and decorating ideas, recipes, songs, and much more.)

*Lucia: Child of Light.* Florence Ekstrand. Welcome Press. (The history and tradition of Sweden's *Lucia* celebration, with tips on creating your own *Lucia* celebration.)

*Lucia Morning in Sweden.* Ewa Rydåker. Illustrated by Carina Ståhlberg. Civilen AB, Halmstad, Sweden. (A Swedish family prepares for Lucia Day in this beautifully illustrated book. Also includes the legend of Lucia, patterns for a Lucia gown, recipes, songs, & more.)

*Lucia Website*: http://www.jeannepasero.com/Christmas/december13.html (A fun website for kids to learn more about St. Lucia and Lucia Day celebrations.)

*A Swedish Christmas CD.* Anne-Charlotte Harvey. Skandisk, Inc. (Songs for a traditional Santa Lucia festival as well as favorite songs for dancing around the Christmas tree.)

*Swedish Christmas.* Catarina Lundgren Åström and Peter Åström. Bokförlaget Arena, Sweden. (Recipes, crafts, and Swedish traditions for the entire Christmas season.)

## Folktales, Culture & Traditions:

*Inger's Promise.* Jami Parkison. Marsh Media. (A beautifully illustrated picture book set among Scandinavia's Sami reindeer herders. Ages 6-10.)

*Mike & Else's Swedish Songbook.* Mike & Else Sevig. Skandisk, Inc. (A collection of 96 songs with piano accompaniment, guitar chords, text and translations. Includes folk songs, Christmas songs, hymns, & more.)

*Scandinavian Girl and Boy Paper Dolls.* Kathy Allert. Dover Publishing, Inc. (Paper dolls with 32 colorful Scandinavian costumes, including 8 Swedish costumes & a Sami costume.)

*The Scandinavian Elves: Their Life and History.* Frid Ingulstad. (The history, and customs of *tomte* or elves, with illustrations by Svein Solem.)

## Vikings:

*Who Were the Vikings?* Jane Chisholm & Straun Reid. EDC Publishing.

*The Story of the Vikings: A Coloring Book.* A. G. Smith. Dover Publishing, Inc.

If you can't find these items at your local library or bookstore, contact *The Tomten Catalog* (1-800-468-2424), or visit our web site (www.skandisk.com).